CW00670387

GuestSpot

CHRISTMAS
Playalong *for* Flute

This publication is not authorised for sale in the
United States of America and/or Canada

WISE PUBLICATIONS
London/New York/Paris/Sydney/Copenhagen/Madrid

Exclusive Distributors:
Music Sales Limited
8/9 Frith Street, London W1V 5TZ, England.
Music Sales Pty Limited
120 Rothschild Avenue, Rosebery, NSW 2018, Australia.

Order No. AM950411
ISBN 0-7119-7025-4
This book © Copyright 1997 by Wise Publications.

Unauthorised reproduction of any part of this publication by
any means including photocopying is an infringement of copyright.

Book design by Michael Bell Design.
Music arranged by Jack Long.
Music processed by Enigma Music Production Services.
Cover photography by George Taylor.

Printed in the United Kingdom by
Page Brothers, Norwich, Norfolk.

CD recorded by Paul Honey.
Instrumental solos by John Whelan.
All keyboards and programming by Paul Honey.

Your Guarantee of Quality:
As publishers, we strive to produce every book to
the highest commercial standards.
The music has been freshly engraved and the book has been
carefully designed to minimise awkward page turns and
to make playing from it a real pleasure.
Particular care has been given to specifying acid-free, neutral-sized
paper made from pulps which have not been elemental chlorine bleached.
This pulp is from farmed sustainable forests and was
produced with special regard for the environment.
Throughout, the printing and binding have been planned to
ensure a sturdy, attractive publication which should give years of enjoyment.
If your copy fails to meet our high standards,
please inform us and we will gladly replace it.

Music Sales' complete catalogue describes thousands of
titles and is available in full colour sections by subject,
direct from Music Sales Limited.
Please state your areas of interest and send a
cheque/postal order for £1.50 for postage to:
Music Sales Limited, Newmarket Road, Bury St. Edmunds, Suffolk IP33 3YB.

Visit the Internet Music Shop at
http://www.musicsales.co.uk

Fingering Guide

Frosty The Snowman

Words & Music by Steve Nelson & Jack Rollins

♩ = 144

Fros - ty the Snow - man was a jol - ly, hap - py soul,___ With a
(Verse 2 see block lyric)

corn cob pipe and a but - ton nose___ and two eyes made out of

coal. Fros - ty the Snow - man is a fai - ry tale they say.

___ He was made of snow, but the child - ren know___ how he came to life one

day. There must have been some mag - ic in that old silk hat they

found, For when they placed it on his head he be - gan to dance a -

- round. Oh, Fros - ty the Snow - man was a - live as he could be.___

© Copyright 1950 Hill and Range Songs Incorporated, USA.
Carlin Music Corporation, Iron Bridge House, 3 Bridge Approach, London NW1
for the British Commonwealth (excluding Canada Australia and New Zealand), Eire and Israel.
All Rights Reserved. International Copyright Secured.

And the child-ren say he could laugh and play— just the same as you and me.

day. He

⊕ CODA

me I'll be back a - - - gain some day.

Verse 2
Frosty the Snowman knew the sun was hot that day,
So he said "Let's run, and we'll have some fun
Now before I melt away".
Down to the village, with a broomstick in his hand,
Running here and there all around the square,
Saying "Catch me if you can".
He led them down the streets of town
Right to the traffic cop,
And he only paused a moment when
He heard him holler "Stop!".
Frosty the Snowman had to hurry on his way,
But he waved goodbye, saying "Don't you cry,
I'll be back again some day".

Hark, The Herald Angels Sing

Christmas Carol

1. Hark, the her - ald

an - gels sing;___ Glo - ry to the new - born King!

Peace on earth and mer - cy mild:___ God and sin - ners

re - con - ciled. Joy - ful, all ye na - tions rise,___

Join the tri - umph of the skies.__ With the'an - gel - ic host pro - claim:

'Christ is___ born in Beth - le - hem'. Hark, the her - ald

© Copyright 1997 Dorsey Brothers Music Limited, 8/9 Frith Street, London W1.
All Rights Reserved. International Copyright Secured.

an - gels sing; Glo - ry — to the new - born King!

Glo - ry — to the new - born King!

Verse 2
Christ, by highest Heav'n adored;
Christ, the everlasting Lord:
Late in time, behold him come,
Offspring of a Virgin's womb.
Veiled in flesh, the Godhead see!
Hail the incarnate Deity!
Pleased as man with man to dwell,
Jesus our Emmanuel!
Hark, the herald angels sing;
Glory to the new-born King!

Verse 3
Hail, the Heaven-born Prince of peace!
Hail the son of righteousness!
Light and life to all He brings,
Risen with healing in his wings.
Mild, He lays his glory by;
Born that man no more may die.
Born to raise the sons of earth;
Born to give them second birth.
Hark, the herald angels sing;
Glory to the new-born King!

Have Yourself A Merry Little Christmas

Words & Music by Hugh Martin & Ralph Blane

Have your-self a mer-ry lit-tle Christ-mas, let your heart be

light; Next year all our trou-bles will be out of sight.

Have your-self a mer-ry lit-tle Christ-mas, make the Yule-tide

gay. Next year all our trou-bles will be miles a - way.

Once a-gain, as in old-en days, hap-py gold-en days of

© Copyright 1944 & 1958 by EMI Feist Corporation, USA.
Worldwide rights controlled by Warner Bros. Publications Incorporated/IMP Limited.
All Rights Reserved. International Copyright Secured.

yore, Faith - ful friends who are dear to us will be near to us once

more. Some - day soon we all will be to - geth - er, if the fates al -

To ⊕ Coda

- low. Un - til then, we'll have to mud - dle through some - how._____

D. 𝄋 al Coda

_____ So have your - self a mer - ry lit - tle Christ - mas now._____

⊕ **CODA** **Slower**

- how._____ So have your - self a

mer - ry lit - tle Christ - mas now._____

Jingle Bells

Traditional

Jin - gle bells, jin - gle bells, jin - gle all the

way; Oh, what fun it is to ride in a one - horse op - en

sleigh. Jin - gle bells, jin - gle bells, jin - gle all the

way; Oh, what fun it is to ride in a one - horse op - en

sleigh. 1. Dash - ing through the snow in a
(Verse 2 see block lyric)

one - horse op - en sleigh: O'er the fields we go,

© Copyright 1997 Dorsey Brothers Music Limited, 8/9 Frith Street, London W1.
All Rights Reserved. International Copyright Secured.

laugh - ing all the way. Bells on bob - tail ring,

mak - ing spi - rits bright: What fun it is to ride and sing a

sleigh - ing song to - night. Jin - gle bells, jin - gle bells,

jin - gle all the way; Oh, what fun it is to ride in a

one - horse op - en sleigh. Jin - gle bells, jin - gle bells,

jin - gle all the way; Oh, what fun it is to ride in a

one - horse op - en sleigh. sleigh. Jin - gle bells,

jin - gle bells, jin - gle all the way; Oh, what fun it

is to ride in a one - horse op - en sleigh. Jin - gle bells,

jin - gle bells, jin - gle all the way; Oh, what fun it

is to ride in a one - horse op - en

sleigh.

Verse 2
Now the ground is white, go it while you're young;
Take the girls tonight, sing this sleighing song.
Get a bob-tailed bay, two-forty for his speed;
Then hitch him to an open sleigh,
And you will take the lead.

Mary's Boy Child

Words & Music by Jester Hairston

Calypso ($\quarternote$ = 100)

Long

time a-go in Beth-le-hem, so the Ho-ly Bi-ble say,

Ma-ry's boy child Je-sus Christ was born on Christ-mas Day.

Hark, now hear the an-gels sing; a new King born to-day. And

Man will live for ev-er-more, Be-cause of Christ-mas Day.

Trum-pets sound and an-gels sing, lis-ten to what they say: That

© Copyright 1956, 1957 Schumann Music Corporation, USA.
Bourne Music Limited, 34-36 Maddox Street, London W1
for Europe, the British Empire and Commonwealth of Nations (excluding Canada).
All Rights Reserved. International Copyright Secured.

Man will live for ev - er - more,— Be - cause of Christ - mas Day.

(Verse 3 see block lyric)

While

shep - herds watched— their flocks by night,— them see a bright new shin - ing star.—

— Them hear a choir— sing, the mus - ic seemed to come— from a -

- far. Now Jo - seph and— his wife, Ma - ry,— come to

Beth - le - hem that night.— Them find no place to

born she child,— Not a sin - gle room— was in sight. Day.

CODA

Slower

Day. Man will live for ev - er - more,— Be -

- cause of Christ - mas Day._____

Verse 3
By and by they find a little nook
In a stable all forlorn;
And, in a manger cold and dark,
Mary's little boy was born.
Long time ago in Bethlehem,
So the Holy Bible say,
Mary's boy child, Jesus Christ,
Was born on Christmas Day.

O Little Town Of Bethlehem

Traditional Christmas Carol

1. O

lit - tle town of Beth - le - hem, how still we___ see thee

lie. A - bove thy deep and dream - less___ sleep, The

si - lent___ stars go by. Yet___ in thy dark___ streets___

shi - - -neth the ev - er - last - ing light. The

hopes and fears of all___ the___ years Are met in___ thee to -

© Copyright 1997 Dorsey Brothers Music Limited, 8/9 Frith Street, London W1.
All Rights Reserved. International Copyright Secured.

night.

2. O

4. **Slow**

- bide— with— us, our Lord Em - ma - nu - el!

Verse 2

O morning stars, together proclaim the holy birth;
And praises sing to God the King,
And peace to men on earth.
For Christ is born of Mary and, gathered all above
While mortals sleep, the angels keep
Their watch of wond'ring love.

Verse 3

How silently, how silently, the wond'rous gift is given!
So God imparts to human hearts
The blessings of His Heaven.
No ear may hear his coming; but, in this world of sin,
Where meek souls will receive Him still
The dear Christ enters in.

Verse 4

O holy child of Bethlehem, descend to us we pray;
Cast out our sin and enter in,
Be born in us today.
We hear the Christmas angels the great good tidings tell.
O come to us, abide with us,
Our Lord Emmanuel!

Once In Royal David's City

Traditional Christmas Carol

1. Once, in Roy-al Da-vid's ci-ty, stood a low-ly cat-tle shed Where a moth-er laid her ba-by in a man-ger for his bed. Ma-ry was that moth-er mild, Jes-us Christ her lit-tle child. 2. He came glad-ness. 5. And our eyes at last shall see Him, Through His own re-deem-ing love. For that child, so dear and gen-tle, is our

(Verses 2. 3. 4. 6. see block lyric)

© Copyright 1997 Dorsey Brothers Music Limited, 8/9 Frith Street, London W1.
All Rights Reserved. International Copyright Secured.

Lord in Heav - en a - bove. And He leads His child - ren

D. %: al Coda

on To the place where he is gone. 6. Not in

CODA **Maestoso**

crowned, All in white, shall wait a - round.

Verse 2
He came down to earth from Heaven,
Who is God and Lord of all;
And His shelter was a stable,
And His cradle was a stall.
With the poor and meek and lowly,
Lived on earth our Saviour holy.

Verse 3
And, through all his wond'rous childhood,
He would honour and obey,
Love and watch the lowly maiden
In whose gentle arms He lay,
Christian children all must be
Mild, obedient, good as He.

Verse 4
For He is our childhood's pattern,
Day by day, like us, He grew.
He was little, weak and helpless;
Tears and smiles, like us, He knew.
And He feeleth for our sadness,
And He shareth in our gladness.

Verse 5
See music.

Verse 6
Not in that poor lowly stable,
With the oxen standing by,
We shall see Him, but in Heaven,
Set at God's right hand on high:
When, like stars, His children, crowned
All in white, shall wait around.

23

Silent Night

Words & Music by Joseph Mohr & Franz Gruber

1. Si - - lent night! Ho - - ly night!
(Verses 2 & 3 see block lyric)

All is calm, all is bright

Round yon Vir - - gin and_____ her child.

Ho - - ly In - -fant, so ten - der and mild,

Sleep in hea - ven - ly peace,_____

© Copyright 1997 Dorsey Brothers Music Limited, 8/9 Frith Street, London W1.
All Rights Reserved. International Copyright Secured.

Sleep in hea - ven - ly peace.

born. (Tacet vocal)

a tempo, espressivo

Poco rit.

a tempo

D. S. al Coda

⊕ CODA

Poco rall.

sa - - ving grace, Jes - us, Lord, at Thy birth;___

a tempo, slower

___ Jes - - us, Lord, at Thy birth!___

Verse 2
Silent night! Holy night!
Shepherds quail at the sight.
Glories stream from Heaven afar;
Heavenly hosts sing Alleluia!
Christ the Saviour is born,
Christ the Saviour is born.

Verse 3
Tacet

Verse 4
Silent night! Holy night!
Son of God, loves pure light:
Radiant beams Thy holy face
With the dawn of saving grace,
Jesus, Lord, at Thy birth;
Jesus, Lord, at Thy birth!

Sleigh Ride

Words by Mitchell Parish
Music by Leroy Anderson

© Copyright 1950 EMI Mills Music Incorporated, USA.
Worldwide print rights controlled by Warner Bros. Publications Incorporated/IMP Limited.
All Rights Reserved. International Copyright Secured.

⊕ CODA

Molto rall.

you.

Verse 2
Outside the snow is falling and friends are calling "Yoo, hoo!";
Come on, it's lovely weather for a sleigh ride together with you.

Verse 4
Let's take that road before us and sing a chorus or two;
Come on, it's lovely weather for a sleigh ride together with you.

Verse 6
There's a happy feeling nothing in the world can buy,
When they pass around the coffee and the pumpkin pie;
It'll nearly be like a picture print by Currier and Ives.
These wonderful things are the things
We remember all through our lives!

Winter Wonderland

Words by Dick Smith
Music by Felix Bernard

Sleigh bells ring, are you list - 'ning?__ In the

lane snow is glist - 'ning,__ A beau - ti - ful sight.__ We're

hap - py to - night__ walk - ing in a win - ter won - der - land.__ Gone a-

- way is the blue - bird.__ Here to stay is a

new bird:__ He sings a love - song__ as we go a - long,__

© Copyright 1997 Dorsey Brothers Music Limited, 8/9 Frith Street, London W1.
All Rights Reserved. International Copyright Secured.

walk - ing in a win - ter won - der - land. In the mea - dow we can build a

snow - man,___ Then pre - tend that he is Par - son Brown.

He'll say "Are you mar - ried?", we'll say "No, man;___ But

you can do the job when you're in town!"___ La - ter on we'll con -

- spire,___ As we dream by the fire,___ To face un - a - fraid___ the

plans that we made,___ Walk - ing in a win - ter won - der - land.___ Sleigh bells

- land To face un - a - fraid___ the plans that we made,

Walk - ing___ in a win - ter___ won - der - land._____

10/99 (35535)

The Beatles

Enya

Phil Collins

Van Morrison

Bob Dylan

Sting

Paul Simon

Tracy Chapman

Eric Clapton

Pink Floyd

New Kids On The Block

Bryan Adams

Tina Turner

Elton John

Bee Gees

Whitney Houston

AC/DC

Bringing you the
words

All the latest in rock and pop.
Plus the brightest and best in West
End show scores. Music books for
every instrument under the sun.
And exciting new teach-yourself
ideas like "Let's Play Keyboard" -
in cassette/book packs, or on video.
Available from all good music shops.

and
music

Music Sales' complete
catalogue lists thousands of
titles and is available free
from your local music shop,
or direct from Music Sales
Limited. Please send a
cheque or postal order for
£1.50 (for postage) to:

Music Sales Limited
Newmarket Road,
Bury St Edmunds,
Suffolk IP33 3YB

Buddy

Five Guys Named Moe

Les Misérables

West Side Story

Phantom Of The Opera

Show Boat

The Rocky Horror Show

**Bringing you the
world's best music.**